Eat the Rainbow

An Adventure in Phytonutrients for Kids of All Ages

Dr. Jonathan Terry

SPEAKING VOLUMES
NAPLES, FLORIDA
2017

Eat the Rainbow

ISBN 978-1-62815-805-2

"To my father,
whose favorite vegetable
was the hot dog."

Acknowledgments

The author and illustrator would like to thank the many families that inspired this work and the characters on their exploration to healthier and more colorful food choices. Dr. Terry would also like to thank those brave young men and women whose enthusiasm leads them to try new fruits and vegetables as they *Eat the Rainbow*.

Meet Landon
an 8-year-old boy,
as you can tell.
Normally he's fine,
but today, he's not feeling well.
Today he's ill.
Today, something is off.
He's got the sniffles
and sneezes—
and wait, here comes a cough!

Mama: What is it this time, Landon?
You don't look too good.
I'm taking you to see the doctor.
This happens more than it should!

The next day,
Landon went to see the doctor.
Sometimes he misses school
to see Dr. Terry.

One quick look, and the doctor
had just one question,
"Are you feeling sick?"
To which Landon said, "Very."

Dr. Terry thought for a moment.

He had to be quick—

not a moment to lose!

He looked up, and he looked down.

He looked all around

looking for clues!

Dr. Terry: I have an idea—

tell me about his lunch.

Mama: Hot dogs and nuggets.

Landon loves to munch!

Dr. Terry: I figured it out!

I know what's wrong.
Let's change what he eats
so he can stay strong.

Mama: What do you mean—
change what he eats?
We watch our diet.
We stay away from sweets!

Dr. Terry: It's not enough,
I'll have you know.
He needs phytonutrients
from colorful fruits and veggies.
Start eating the rainbow!
Not to be rude,
but it starts with the food.

Mama: Start eating the rainbow?
I'll do my part.
But, Dr. Terry—I need some help.
Where do I start?

12

Eating the Rainbow
is nothing to dread.

Let's start here,
with food that is red.

Start eating these,
and you'll stop getting sick.
Grapes and cherries—
they're all fantastic!

How many of these do you know?

Apple, Red Beans, Beets,
Bell Pepper, Blood Oranges,
Cranberries, Cherries, Grapefruit,
Goji Berries, Grapes, Onions,
Plums, and Pomegranates.

Orange is next—
didn't you know?

Pretty soon, you'll be a pro!
These foods are good—
they'll keep your tummy clean.

There are carrots, mangoes
and my favorites—nectarines!

How many of these do you know?

Apricots, Bell Peppers, Cantaloupe, Carrots, Mangoes, Nectarines, Oranges, Papayas, Persimmons, Pumpkin, Squash, Sweet Potatoes, Tangerines, Turmeric, and Yams.

20

Are you keeping up?
Don't be slow.

Next in line . . .
is the color yellow.

Look at all these—
aren't they cute?

Lemon, banana, corn
and star fruit!

How many of these do you know?

Apples, Asian Pears, Bananas,
Bell Peppers, Corn, Ginger,
Lemons, Millet, Pineapples,
Potatoes, Star Fruit,
Succotash, and Summer Squash.

24

To play in sports,
you must be lean.

The next fruits and veggies
are the color green.

This is exciting—
go on and shout!

Celery, cucumbers, limes
and sprouts!

How many of these do you know?

Apples, Artichokes, Asparagus, Avocadoes, Bamboo Sprouts, Bean Sprouts, Bell Peppers, Bitter Melon, Bok Choy, Broccoli, Broccolini, Brussels Sprouts, Cabbage, Celery, Cucumbers, Soybeans, Green Beans, Green Peas, Green Tea, Leafy Greens, Limes, Okra, Olives, Pears, Snow Peas, Watercress, Zucchini.

Look for foods
with nutritional value.

Purple, **black**, and blue!
Who knew?

There are a lot of colors.
Don't worry—it's not scary!

I see **eggplant**, kale,
and a **blackberry**!

How many of these do you know?

Bell Peppers, Berries, Beets, Cabbage, Carrots, Cauliflower, Eggplants, Figs, Grapes, Kale, Olives, Plums, Potatoes, Prunes, Raisins, and **Black Rice**.

The foods get brighter
and their colors lighter.

Don't be coy.
Just try the soy.

There are more to choose from.
Aren't you fortunate?

Try the garlic, the ginger—
and look, is that a coconut?

How many of these do you know?

Apples, Beans, Cauliflower, **Cocoa**, Coconuts, **Coffee**, **Dates**, Garlic, Ginger, Jicama, Legumes, Lentils, Mushrooms, **Nuts**, Onions, Pears, Sauerkraut, Seeds, Shallots, Soy, Tahini, **Tea**, and Whole Grains.

Landon: I'm not sick anymore!
Didn't you hear?

I'm eating the rainbow,
and I'm in the clear!

Red and orange, yellow,
and green—

I'm eating them all,
and I feel pristine!

I added foods of all colors,
plus brown, tan and white.

I feel so good—
I could fly a kite!

Don't forget—
the blue, purple, and black!

With these colors,
I must be clever.

Thanks to these, I'm not only back,
but I'm better than ever!

40

This Eat the Rainbow coloring book
is the perfect interactive
supplement to our full-color storybook.
Learn the rainbow through some of
the brightest and most delicious colors in nature!

For more information
visit: www.speakingvolumes.us

About the Author and Illustrator

Jonathan Terry, DO, ABIHM is a board-certified osteopathic physician and surgeon, a general psychiatrist, a Diplomate of the American Board of Psychiatry and Neurology (ABPN), a Diplomate of the National Board of Physicians and Surgeons (NBPAS), and a Diplomate of the American Board of Integrative Holistic Medicine (ABIHM). He is involved in the certification process through the Institute for Functional Medicine (IFM). Dr. Terry is proud to be a National Health Service Corps Ambassador and works primarily with underserved and migrant worker populations, high-acuity inpatient psychiatric patients, and in consultation for program and policy-building initiatives. Dr. Terry's clinical interests include primary care consultation, nutrition, osteopathy, integrative medicine, strength-based therapies, and prevention. His favorite fruit is the avocado. Read more at www.DrJonathanTerry.com.

Davida L. Simon Terry holds an M.A. in Communication, and has taught bilingual education and English as a second language. Ms. Simon Terry is a writer, columnist, radio talk-show host and owns an advertising agency with expertise in creating and producing in both English and Spanish, radio and television commercials and documentaries. As an illustrator, she created the artwork for Chicago's Field Museum of Natural History botanical publications. She has also published her own greeting and note cards depicting wildlife in watercolor and gouache in an effort to protect and create a reverence for these animals. Her favorite vegetables are beets, and her favorite fruits are peaches, pineapples, and bananas. Davida L. Simon Terry is Dr. Jonathan Terry's mom; she first introduced him to fruits and vegetables many years ago.

Made in the USA
San Bernardino, CA
17 November 2018